D1469341

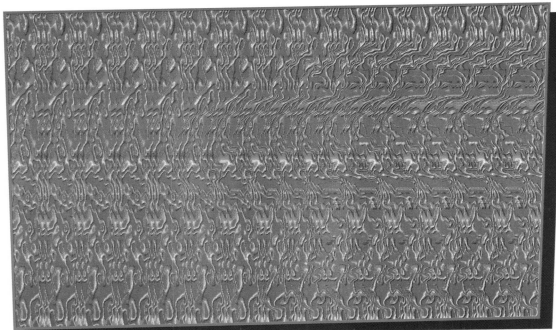

Written by James DiGiovanna

Art by TXF Graphics

SPACE JAM, characters, names and all related indicia are trademarks of Warner Bros. © 1996
Copyright © 1996 Modern Publishing, a division of Unisystems, Inc. TM Eye Illusions is a trademark of Modern Publishing, a division of Unisystems, Inc.
® Honey Bear Books is a trademark owned by Honey Bear Productions, Inc., and is registered in the U.S. Patent and Trademark Office.

Modern Publishing
A Division of Unisystems, Inc.
New York, New York 10022
Printed in the U.S.A.

SJM028

© 1996 Warner Bros.

INTRODUCTION

Welcome to a new world! Hidden within the beautiful abstract patterns in this book are exciting three-dimensional images. All you need to do is look at the patterns in a special way, relax, and the images will pop out at you as if by magic. You might even be tempted to reach out and touch them.

The wonderful images in this book are called "stereograms." They are flat, two-dimensional pictures that, when viewed in the right way, appear to have three dimensions. Early 3-D pictures were really two images, and you needed special glasses or a special viewer to look at them. Thanks to modern computer technology, stereograms are now single images that can be viewed directly by anyone!

For hundreds of years, scientists have been studying how vision works. Artists began using this knowledge to draw 3-D pictures over 150 years ago, but since they drew by hand, it took them a long time to create even one image. The development of computers changed everything.

Starting in the 1960s, artists used computer graphics to create increasingly complex and beautiful 3-D art. At first, the 3-D images were simple shapes and designs. As computer graphic technology improved, and as the artists grew in their craft, more detailed and exciting pictures were created.

We can see these pictures in three dimensions because all human beings have "binocular" vision. Our eyes are several inches apart, so each eye sees things from a slightly different angle. This information is combined in the brain to give us a 3-D view of the world. Things not only have height and width, they have depth as well. Stereograms, though they look like simple abstract patterns, actually contain all the information the brain needs to see a 3-D image. The information for the right eye is on the right side of the picture, and that for the left eye is on the left side. By relaxing the focus of our eyes, we allow the two sides to overlap, and the brain is tricked into seeing a 3-D picture.

It's a simple idea made possible thanks to complex technology. Truly, these 3-D pictures show us a new world!

INSTRUCTIONS

To see these 3-D images, you need the right setting. First, find a quiet place with bright lighting, and make sure the picture you look at is evenly lit. Then sit up straight, take a deep breath, and relax. This is very important. The more relaxed you are, the easier it will be to find the images, and the more fun you will have. Also, be patient, especially in the beginning. It may take several minutes before you can see the picture in three dimensions. So take it easy and don't give up.

There are several ways of viewing the 3-D images in this book:

Method One

Begin by looking at the cover picture. The cover is shiny, and you should be able to see your reflection, or the reflection of a light in it. Look at the picture on the cover, but focus your eyes on the reflection. This will make your eyes relax and go out of focus. Stare at the picture for a minute or two until you feel something start to happen. Just relax, continue staring, and the 3-D image will appear.

Method Two

Another way to see the 3-D image is to bring the picture right up to your nose. Don't try to see the image — just let your eyes go completely out of focus. Then, while keeping your eyes out of focus, move the picture back to about arm's length. Keep looking at it with your eyes relaxed, and after a little while the 3-D image will pop out.

Method Three

A third approach is to try and see through the picture. Look at the page, relax your eyes, and imagine you are looking beyond the book. Keep looking for a few minutes. Remember, patience is important. So is relaxation. Just take it easy and enjoy yourself. In time, a beautiful 3-D image will appear to you.

These three methods make up the parallel-viewing technique. There is also a cross-eyed technique that is more comfortable for some people.

Method Four

To view the images in the cross-eyed way, bring your finger, or a pen or pencil, up close to your eyes. Focus on the finger, pen or pencil. As you hold this focus, look at the stereogram. It may take a few minutes, but the 3-D image will appear.

Once you develop one technique, try to develop the others. Sometimes, different techniques allow you to see slightly different images in the same stereogram. For example, if you look at a 3-D image of birds flying in the sky, the parallel-viewing technique may show you the birds in front, with the clouds in the background. With the cross-eyed technique, however, you may see the clouds in front, looking as if the birds have already flown through them leaving bird-shaped holes!

There are 14 images in this book, each with a riddle to help you discover what it is. If you're patient and keep at it, you will soon be able to see all of them. Then you truly will be an expert in the world of 3-D!

Opposite:

**Holding his weapon he yells out loud,
"You're joining Swackhammer's outer-space crowd!"
He thinks it makes him a tough little one,
To zap poor earthlings with a raygun!**

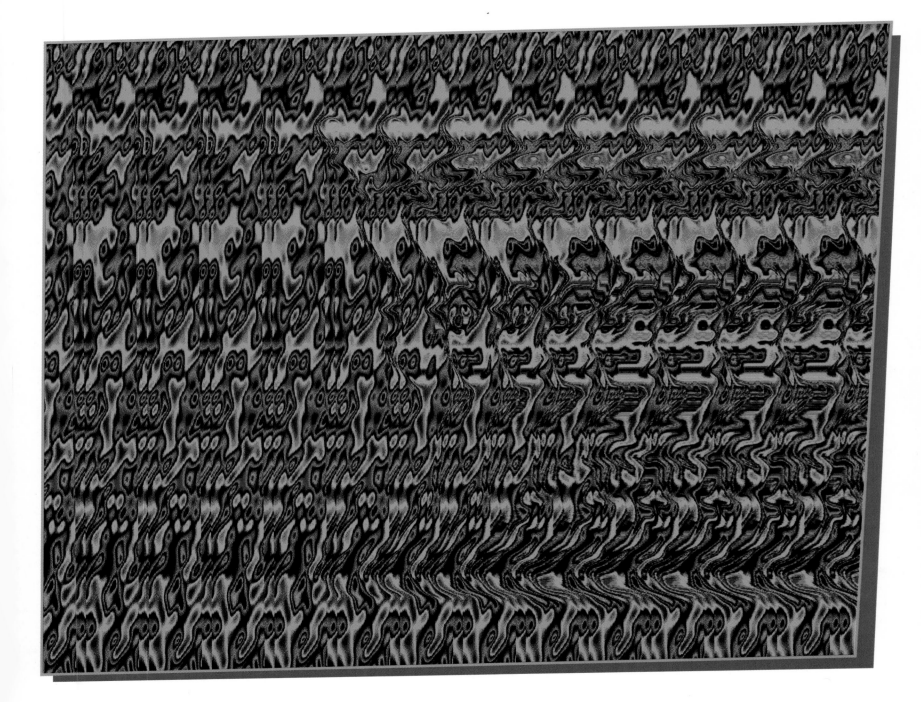

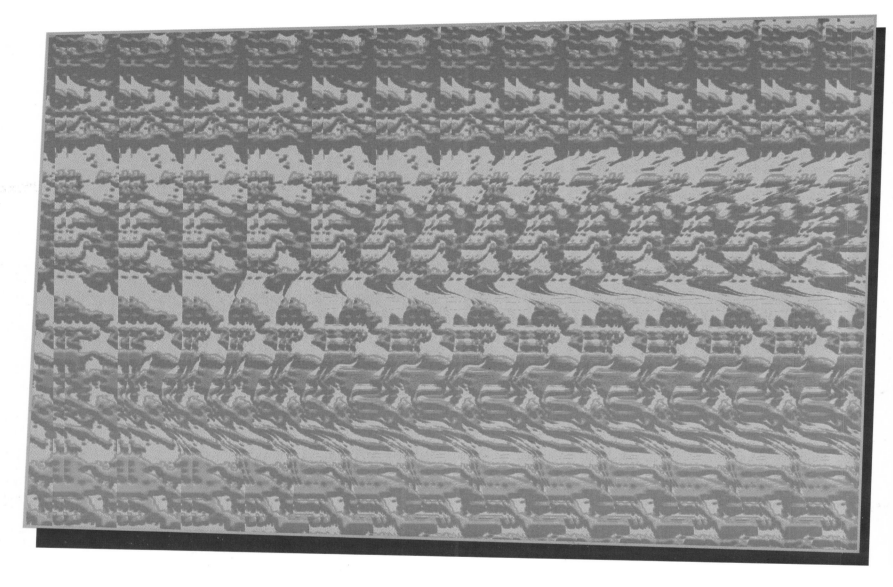

Here's a runner we all know,
From our favorite cartoon show!
He'll play all day without making a peep,
Till the ball goes in, then he says "Meep! Meep!"

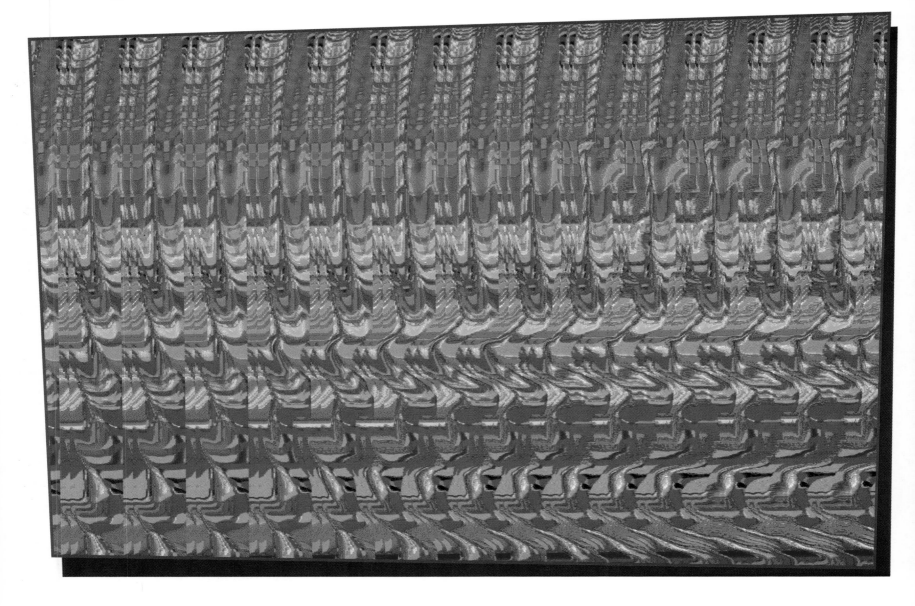

What could be worse than this furry face,
Chasing a Road Runner all over space?
A bad mechanic blames his tool,
This guy blames Acme for looking the fool!

He's porcine, portly, and
pretty much pink,
He stutters and stammers to
say what he thinks!
But when it is time for a
basketball game,
He plays like he's come from
the hall of fa-fame!

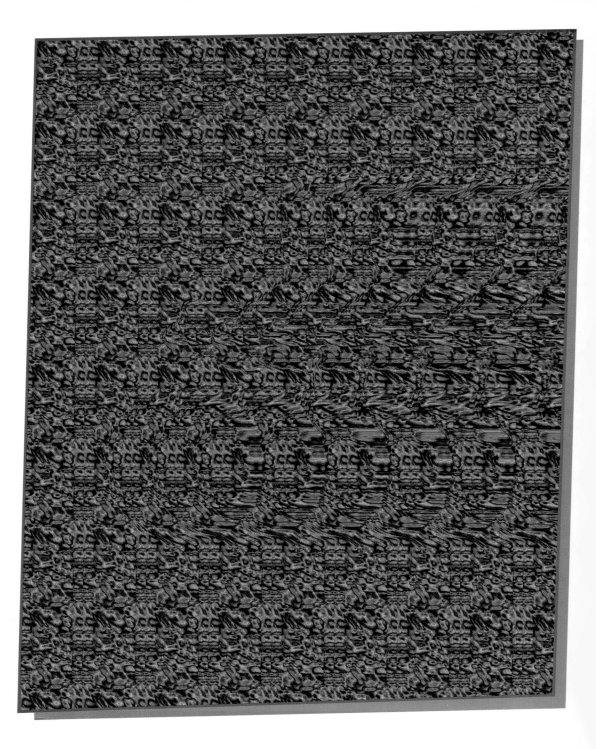

She looks good in shorts,
And has great big ears!
She excels in sports,
And drives Bugs to tears!

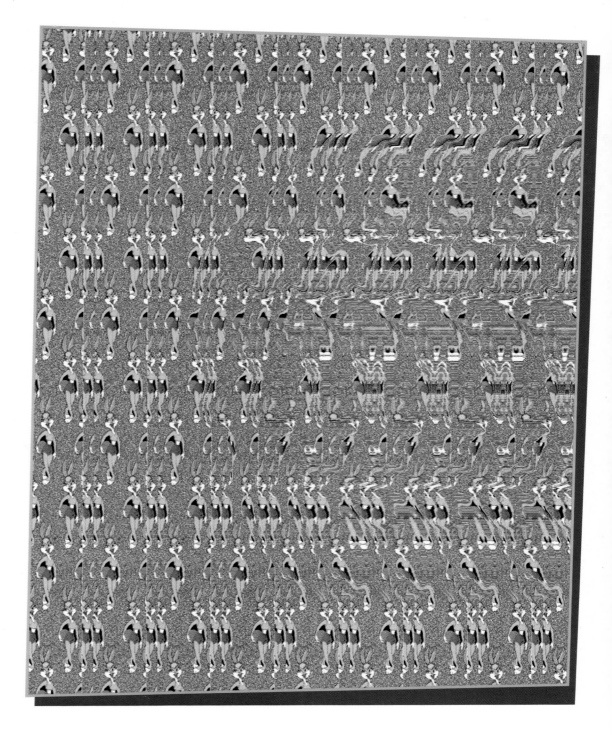

Top duck coming through!

Opposite:

Hunting for wabbits is his favowite sport,
But now he must wun 'cwoss the basketball court
He hopes that he wins for one vewy good weason
When this game is over – it's duck-hunting season

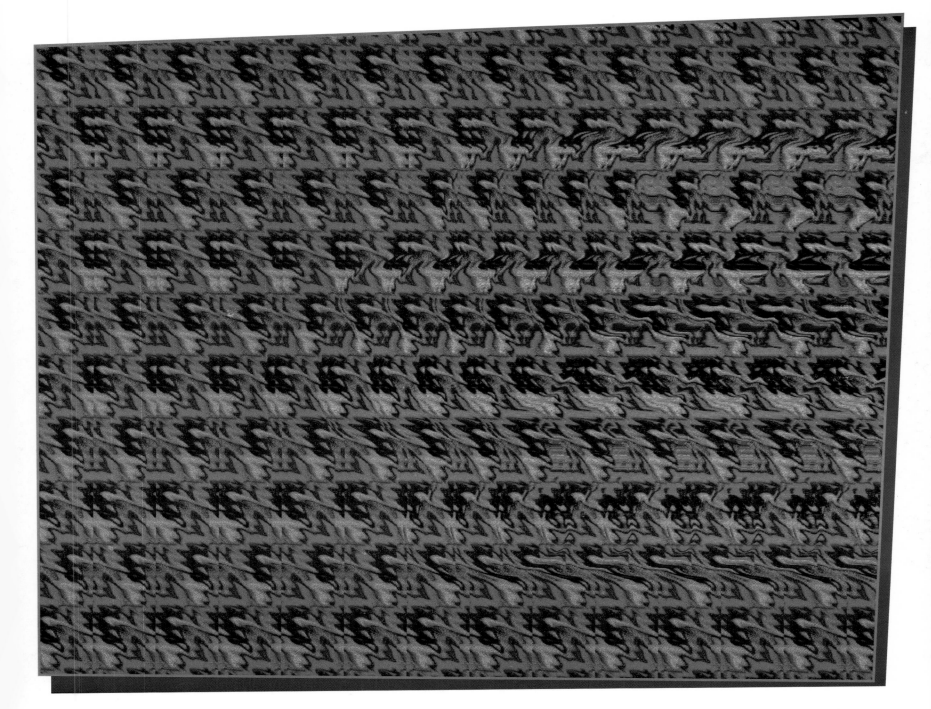

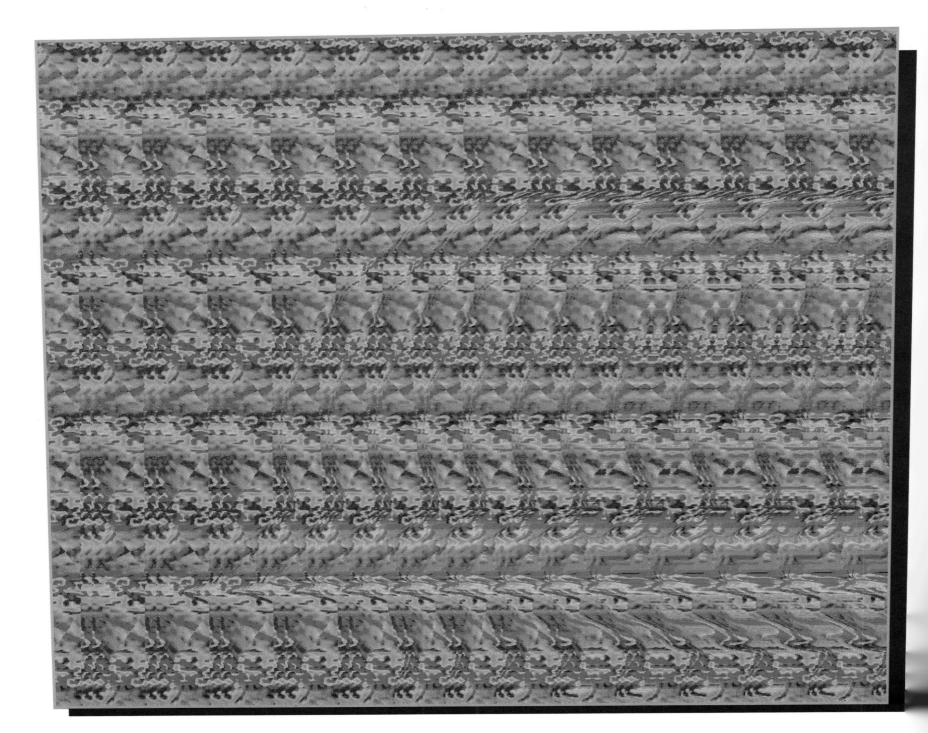

Opposite:

He'll shoot his six guns up in the air
As he grabs his mustache (it's red, like his hair)!
He says "This universe tain't big enough
Fer galoots and Nerdlucks," and goes for the stuff!

"Maybe there is no intelligent life out there in the universe after all."

Overleaf:

He likes to eat carrots, he's big-eared and gray,
He's the team-leader of Looneys today!
He rests on the bench, getting ready to rock,
You'll know that it's him when he says, "What's up, Doc?"

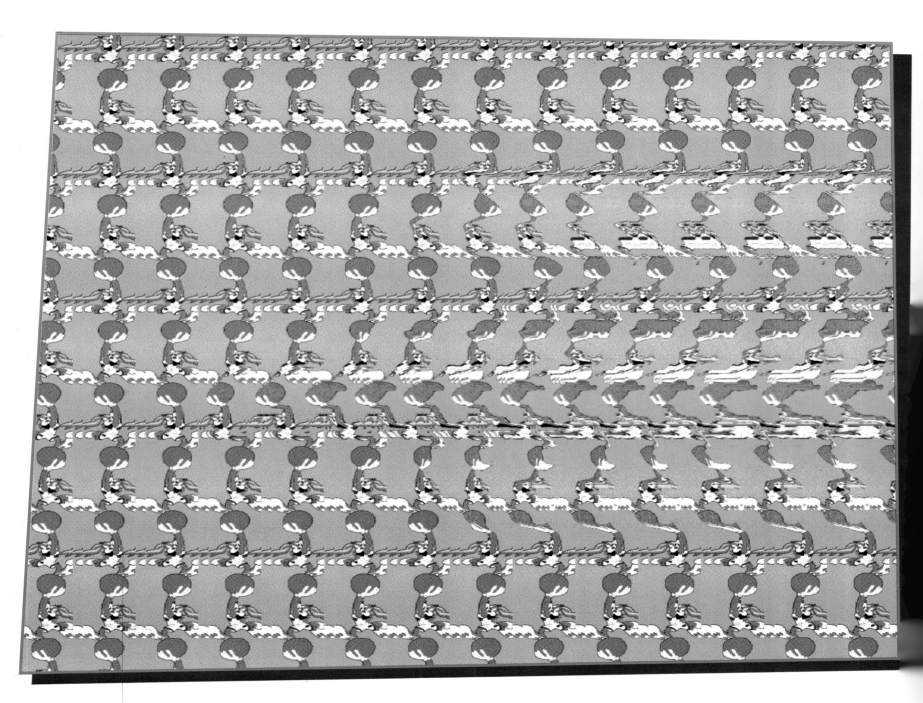

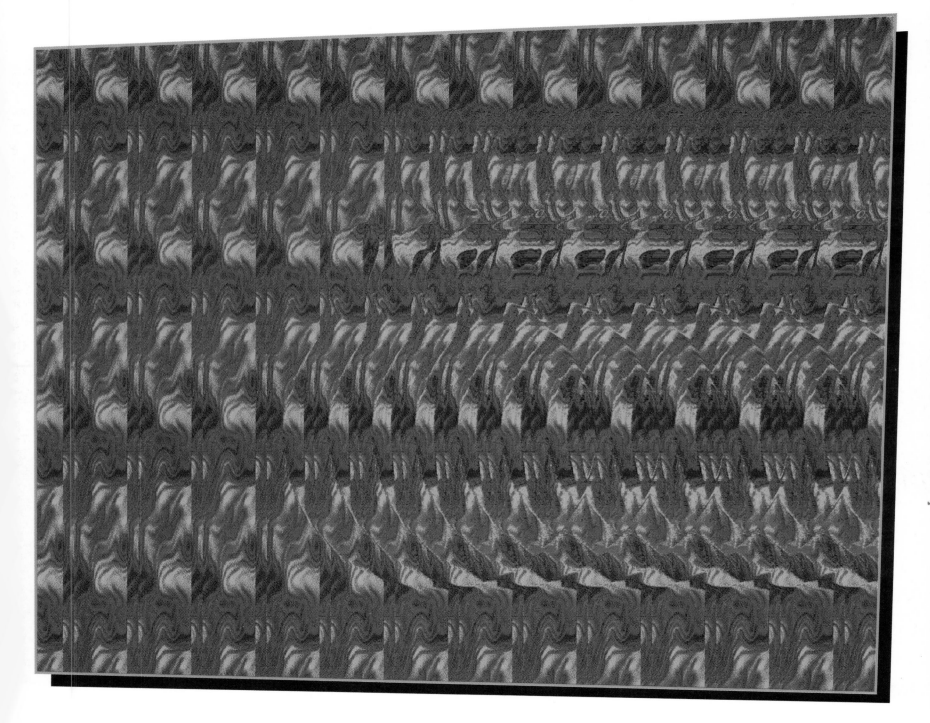

Previous page:

This little tweeter will show one and all
That small yellow birds play great basketball!
He'll fly with the ball in his tiny beak,
Then he'll shoot and score like a real super-freak!

Very funny. Let's all laugh at the duck.

Opposite:

With the tail of a dino and big, frightened eyes,
He's looking so timid, you think he might cry!
He's got tiny arms and he shakes with deep fear,
When that evil bouncer, Swackhammer, appears!

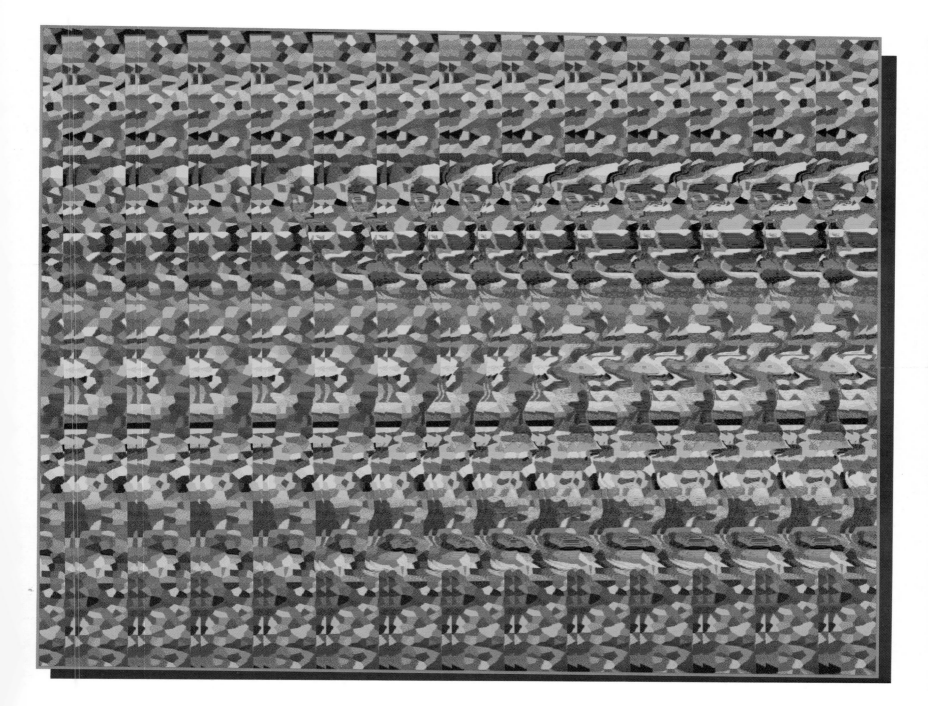

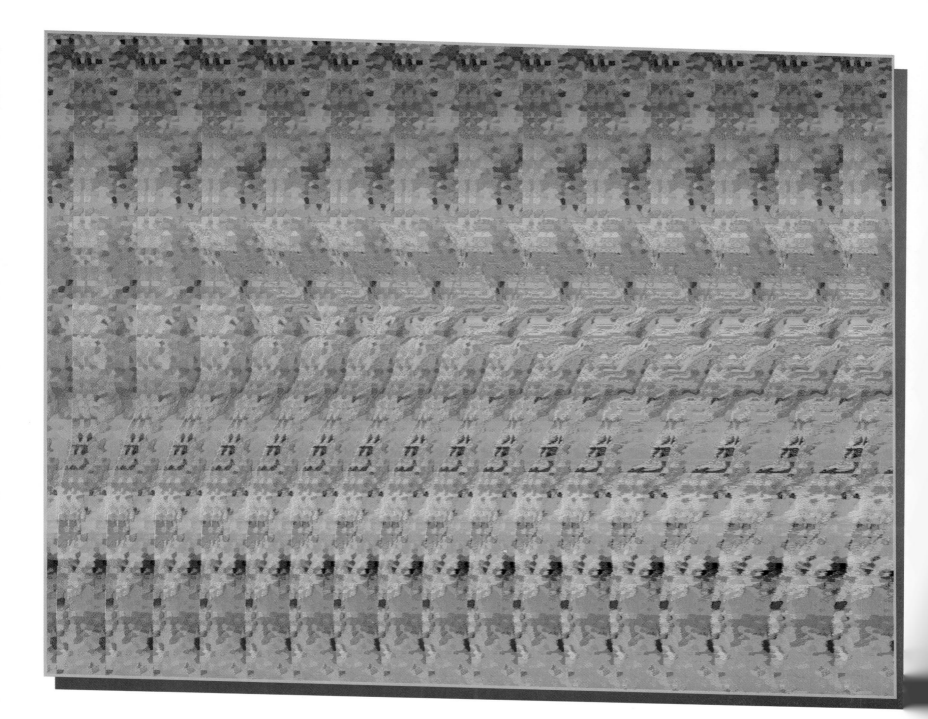

Let the games begin!

Opposite:

This is the evil, grinning face
Of a suit-wearing villain from outer space!
He's fat, ugly, and mean as a shark,
He runs the galaxy's worst themeless park!

19

He mumbles, rumbles,
   whirls round and round,
He spins his way right
   through the rocks in the ground!
He's a devilish critter
   from a down-under place,
All set to play b-ball
   in outerest-space!

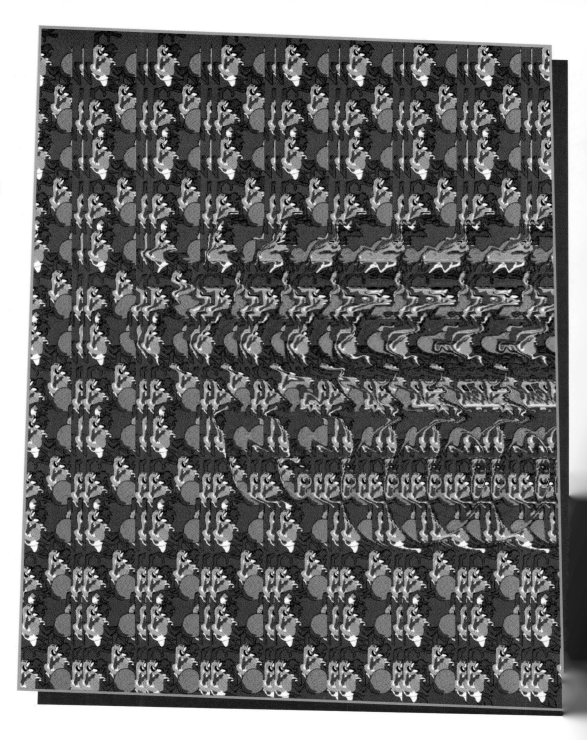

Bustin' a move on
the basketball court,
Swackhammer hates him
and yells "Hissy-Boo!"
He's short, but he has
a knack for this sport,
He's the home-kitty
shooting for two!

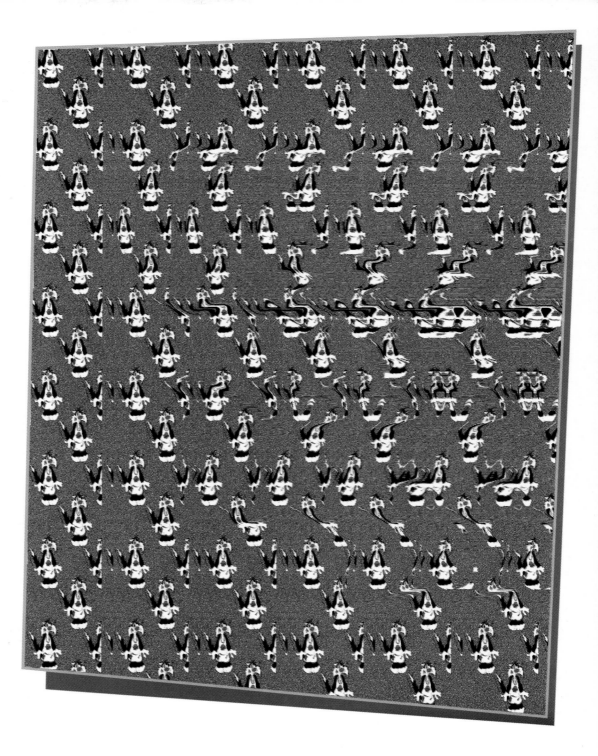

Get ready to jam!

Opposite:

There's a very strange smell at half-court today
Where that French-talkin' player is at!
The other team's players are running away,
From le stinky black-and-white cat!

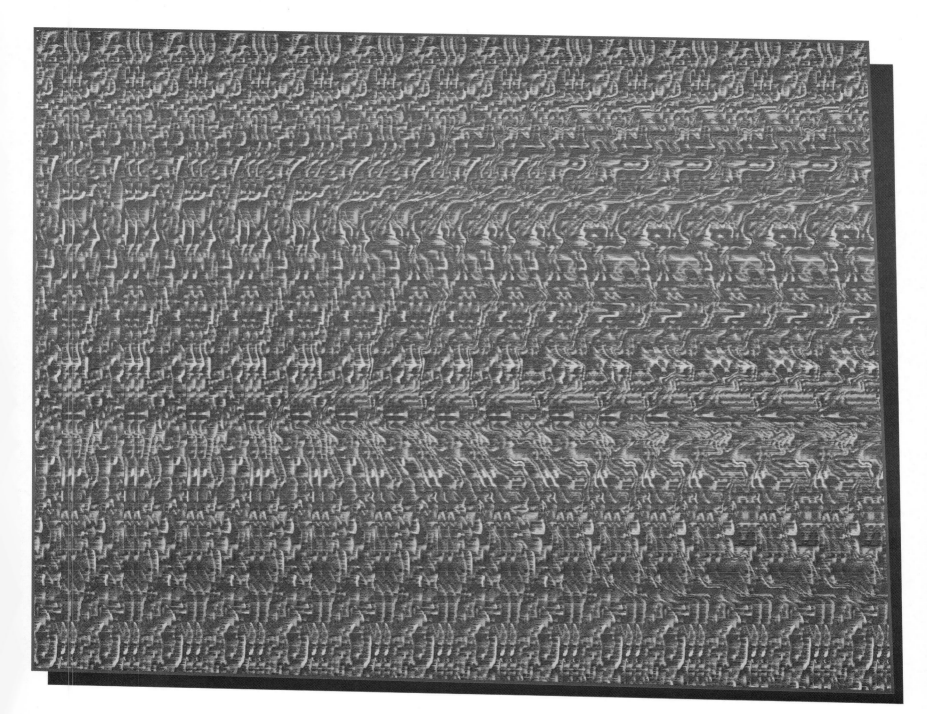

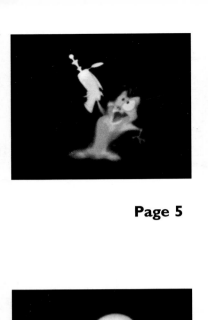

Page 5

Page 6

Page 7

Page 8

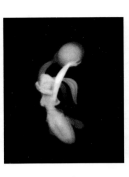

Page 9

Page 11

Page 12

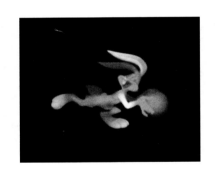

Page 14

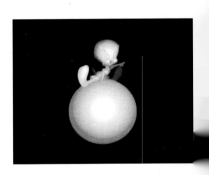

Page 15

Page 17

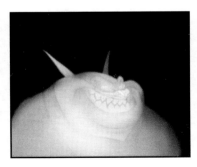

Page 18

Page 20

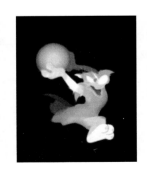

Page 21

Page 2